# Time to Sign with Music

## Toddler-Preschooler

# "ABC's"

(Slow Version Traditional, Illustrations Copyright©2002 Time to Sign, Inc.)

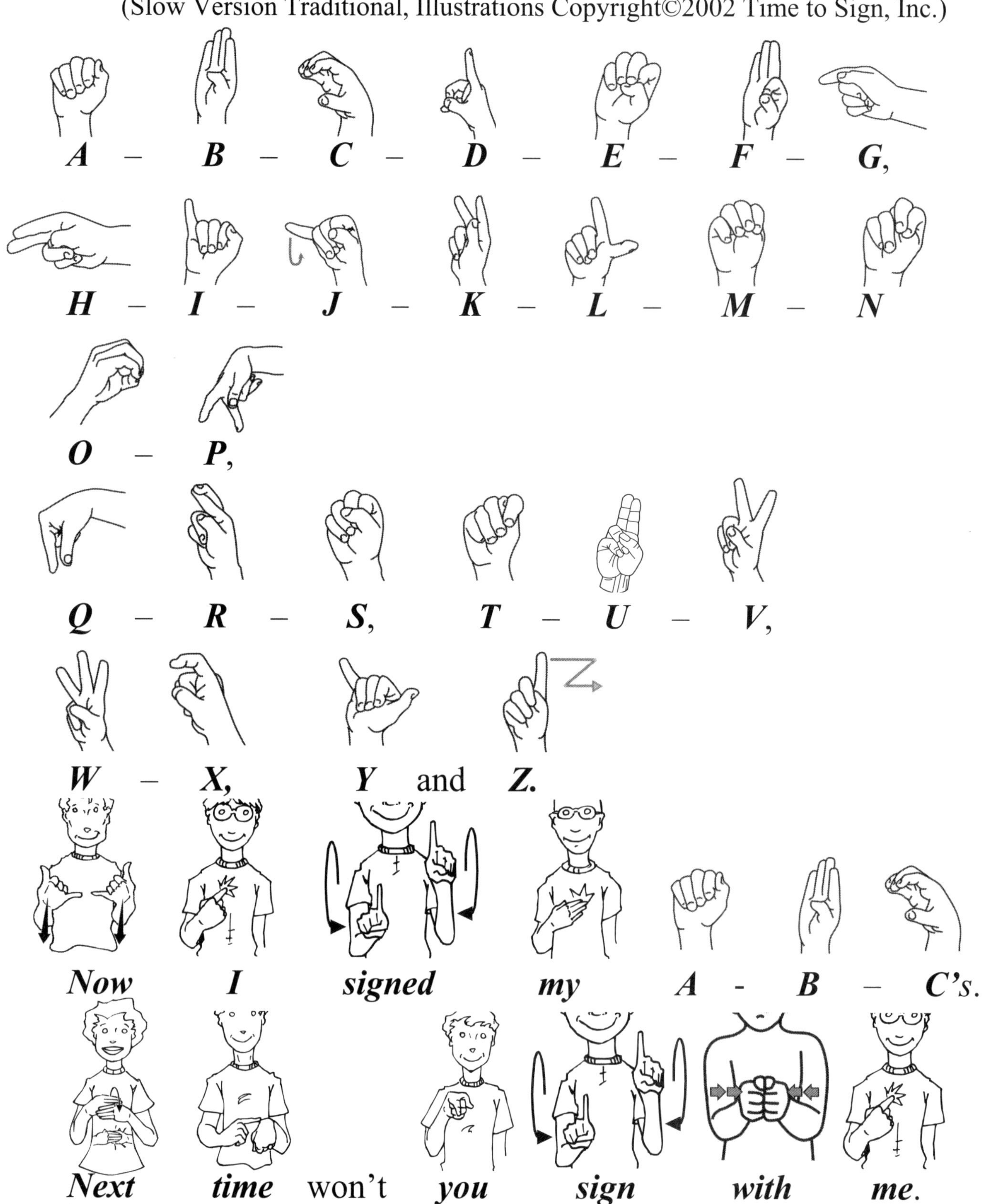

# “ABC’s”

(Traditional, Illustrations Copyright©2002 Time to Sign, Inc.)

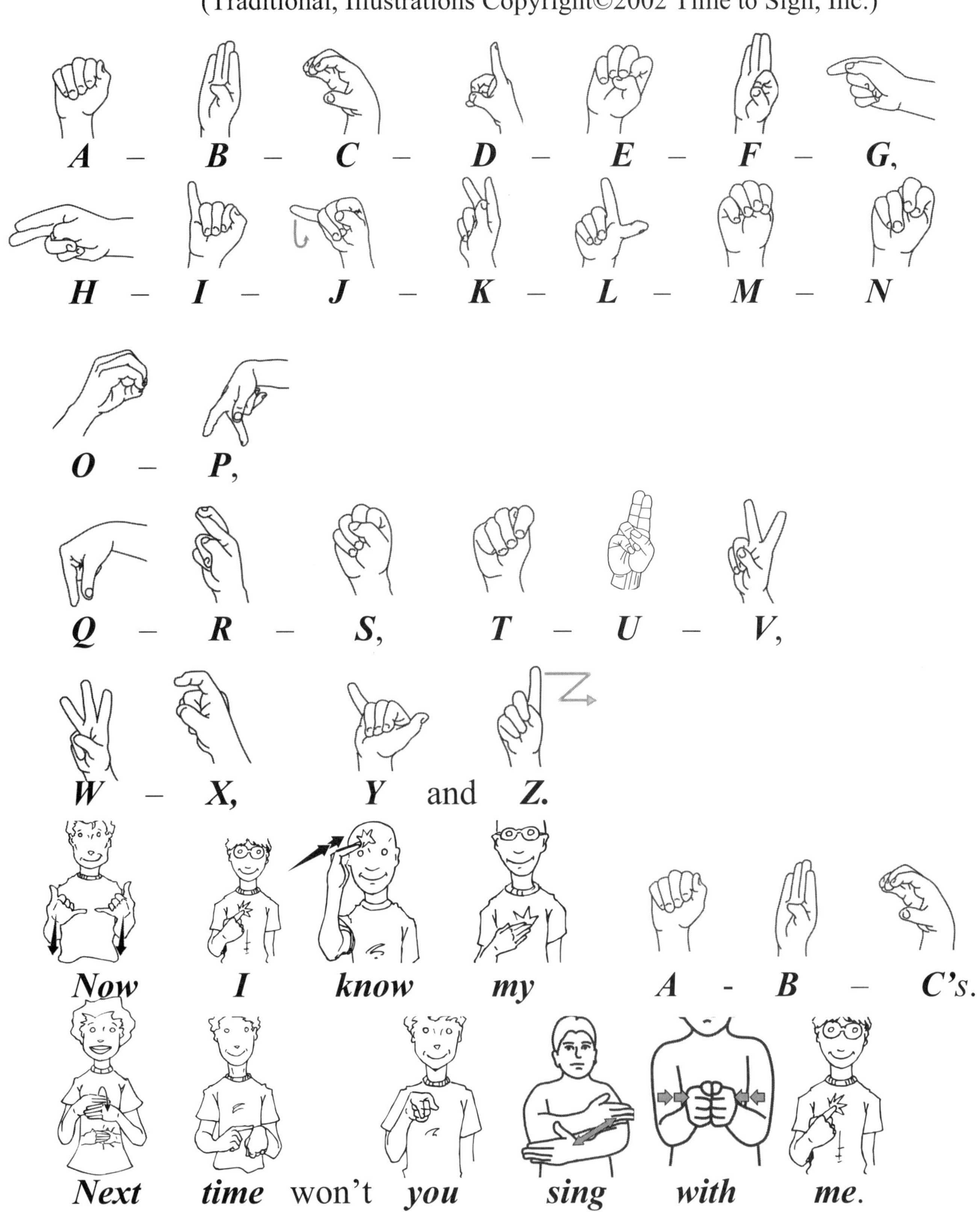

# "Bingo"

(Traditional, Illustrations Copyright©2002 Time to Sign, Inc.)

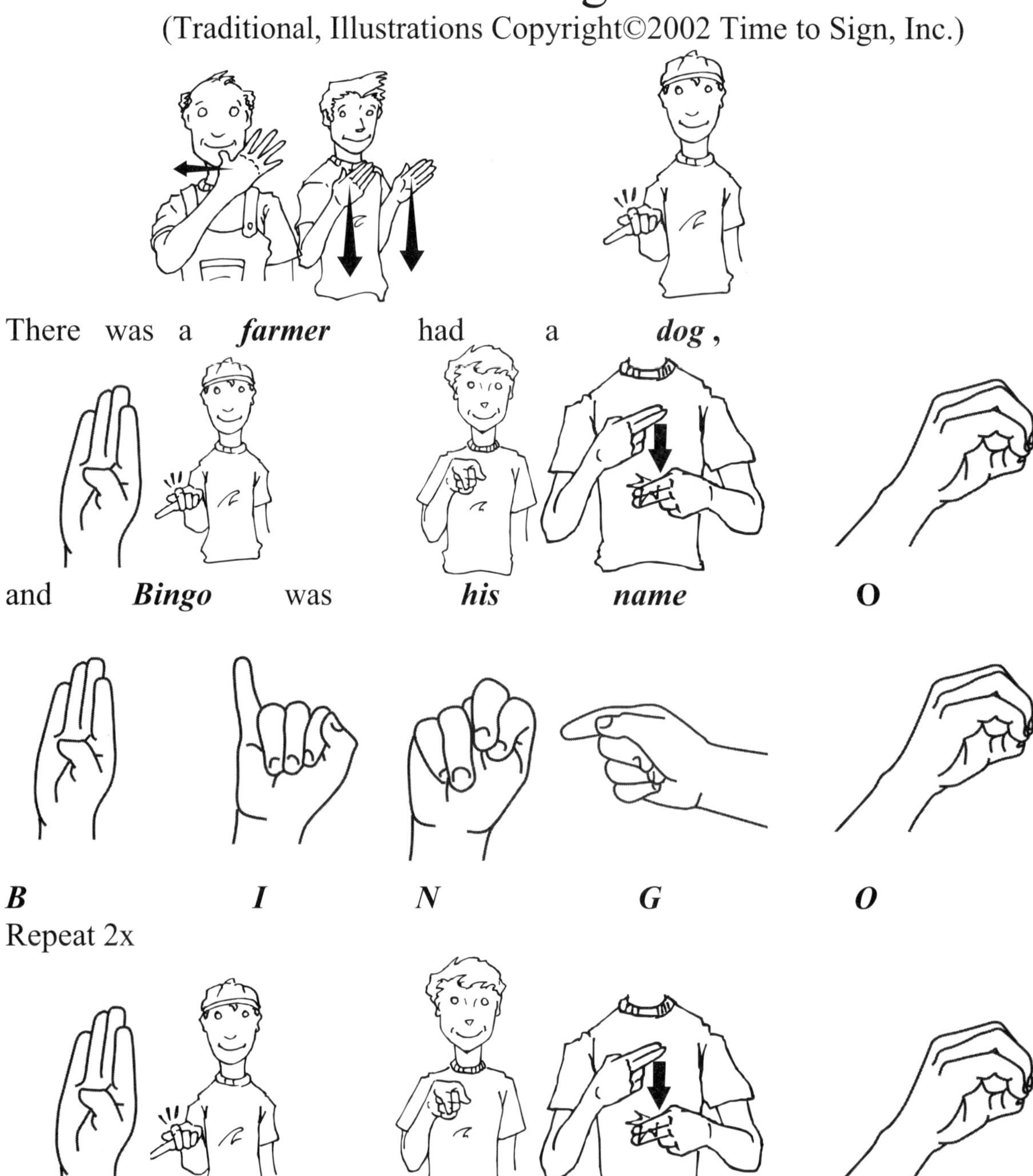

There was a ***farmer*** had a ***dog***,

and ***Bingo*** was ***his*** ***name*** **O**

***B*** ***I*** ***N*** ***G*** ***O***

Repeat 2x

and ***Bingo*** was ***his*** ***name*** ***O.***

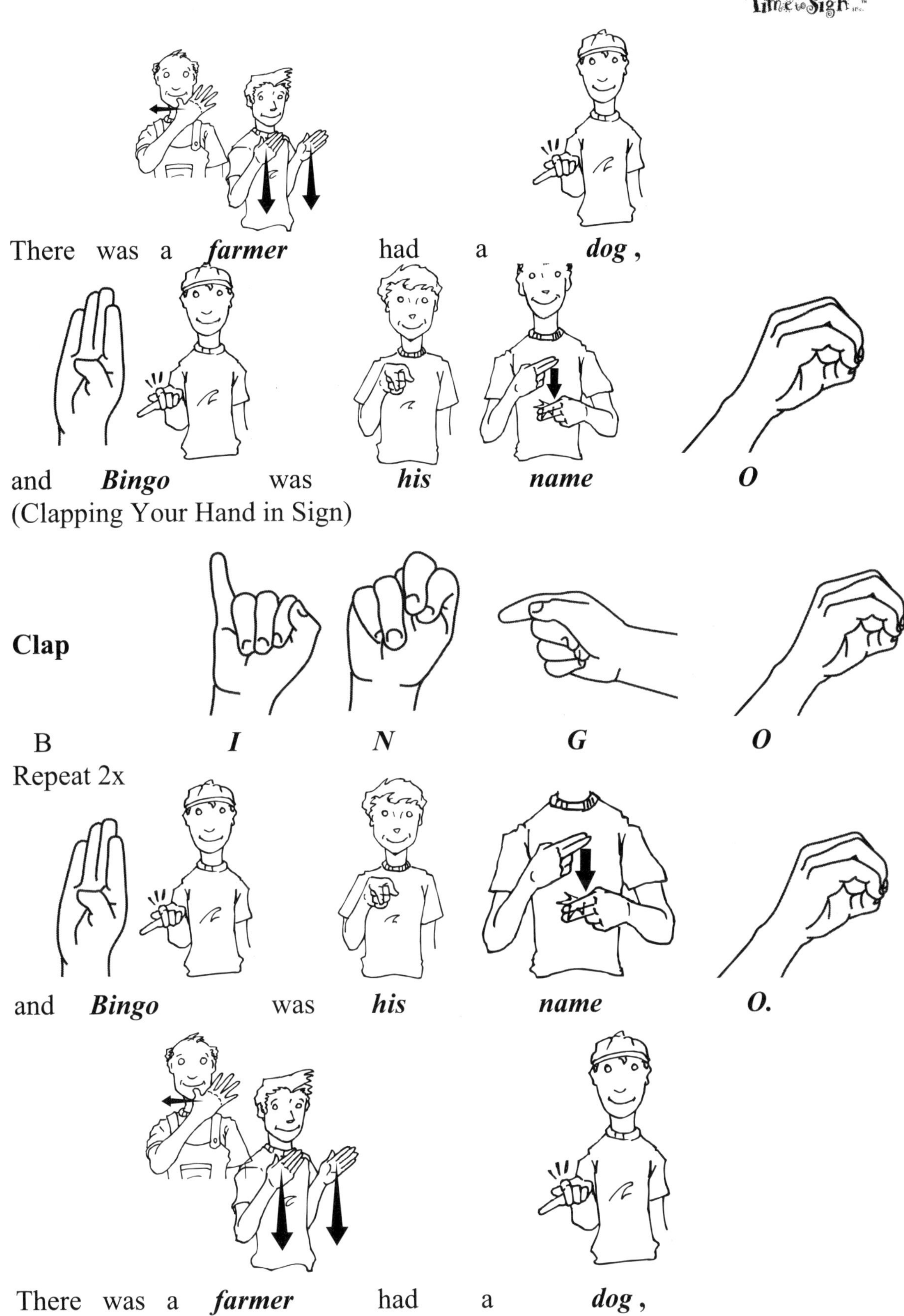

There was a ***farmer*** had a ***dog***,

and ***Bingo*** was ***his*** ***name*** ***O***

(Clapping Your Hand in Sign)

**Clap**

B ***I*** ***N*** ***G*** ***O***

Repeat 2x

and ***Bingo*** was ***his*** ***name*** ***O.***

There was a ***farmer*** had a ***dog***,

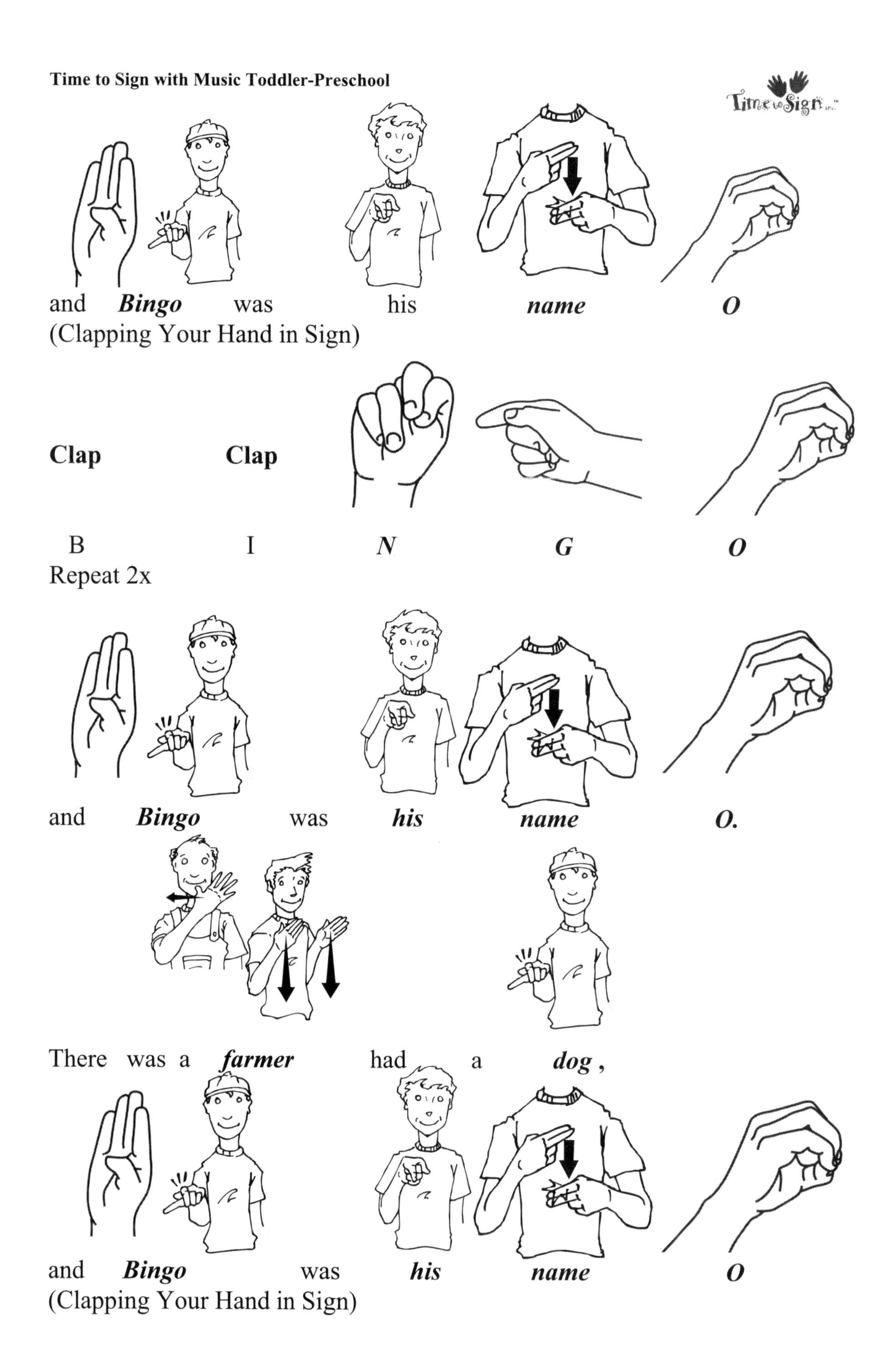


and ***Bingo*** was his ***name*** ***O***
(Clapping Your Hand in Sign)

**Clap** **Clap**

B I ***N*** ***G*** ***O***
Repeat 2x

and ***Bingo*** was ***his*** ***name*** ***O.***

There was a ***farmer*** had a ***dog*** ,

and ***Bingo*** was ***his*** ***name*** ***O***
(Clapping Your Hand in Sign)

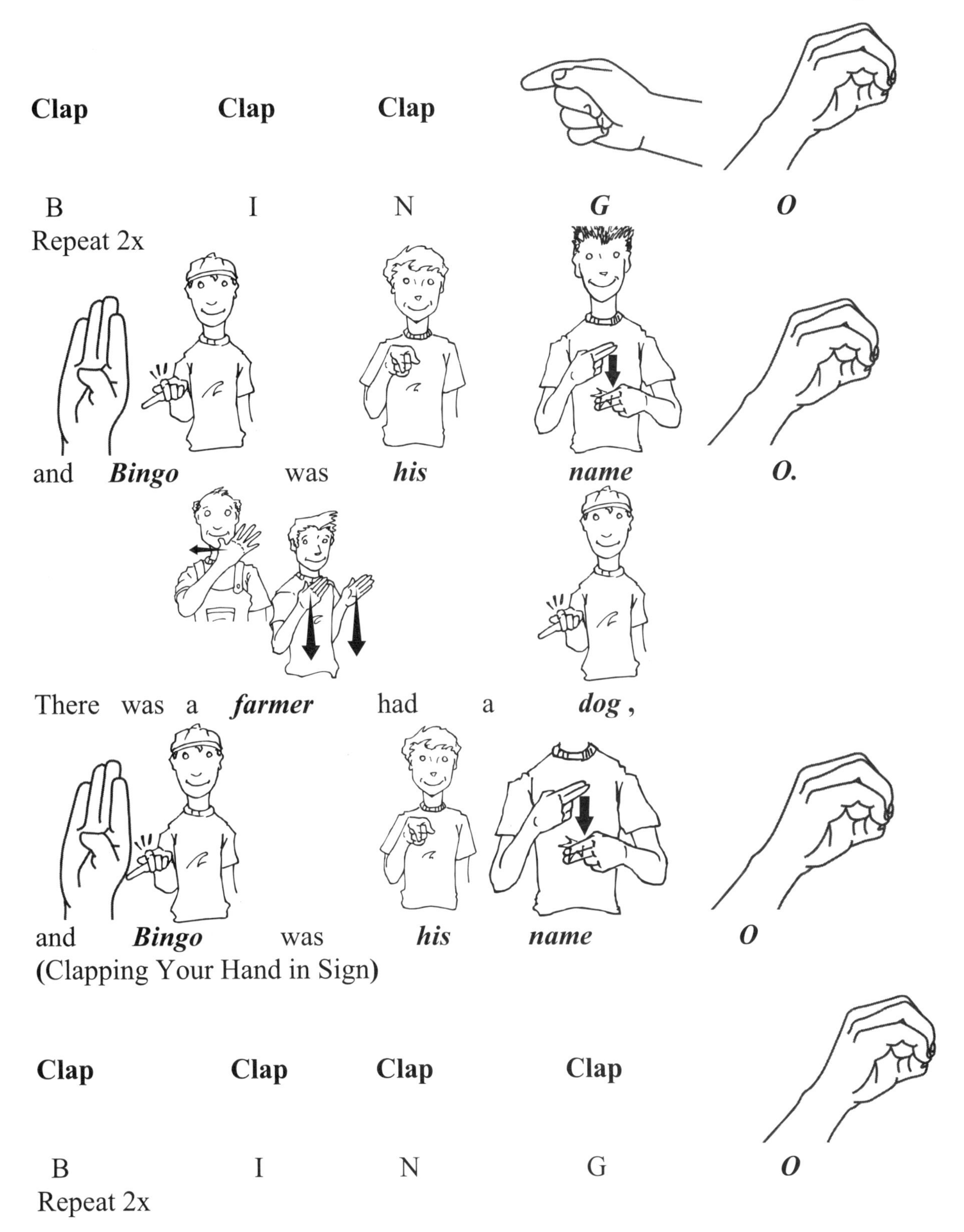

**Clap** **Clap** **Clap**

B I N ***G*** ***O***
Repeat 2x

and ***Bingo*** was ***his*** ***name*** ***O.***

There was a ***farmer*** had a ***dog*** ,

and ***Bingo*** was ***his*** ***name*** ***O***
**(**Clapping Your Hand in Sign**)**

**Clap** **Clap** **Clap** **Clap**

B I N G ***O***
Repeat 2x

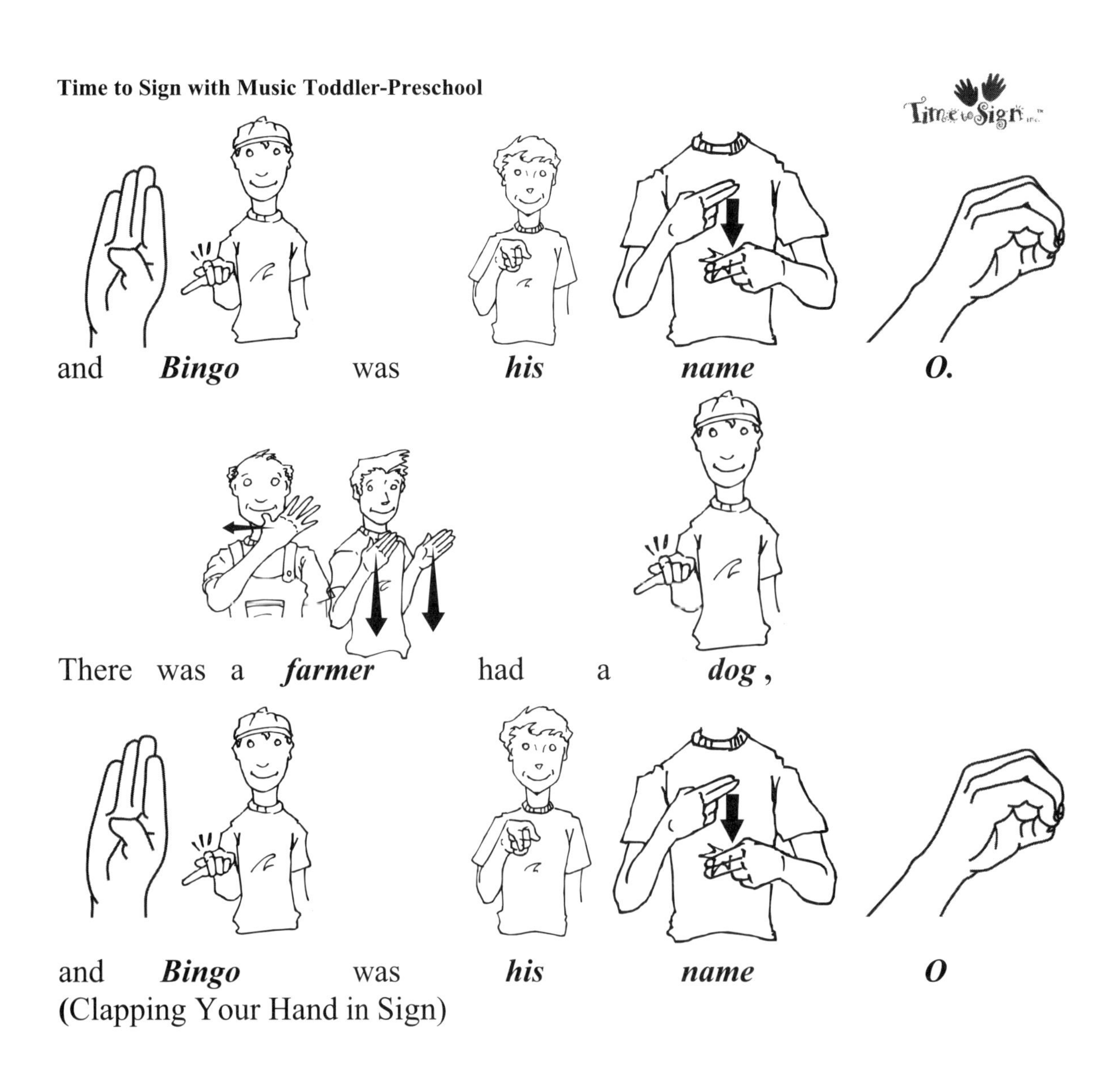


and ***Bingo*** was ***his*** ***name*** ***O.***

There was a ***farmer*** had a ***dog*** ,

and ***Bingo*** was ***his*** ***name*** ***O***
(Clapping Your Hand in Sign)

**Clap** **Clap** **Clap** **Clap** **Clap**

B I N G O
Repeat 2x

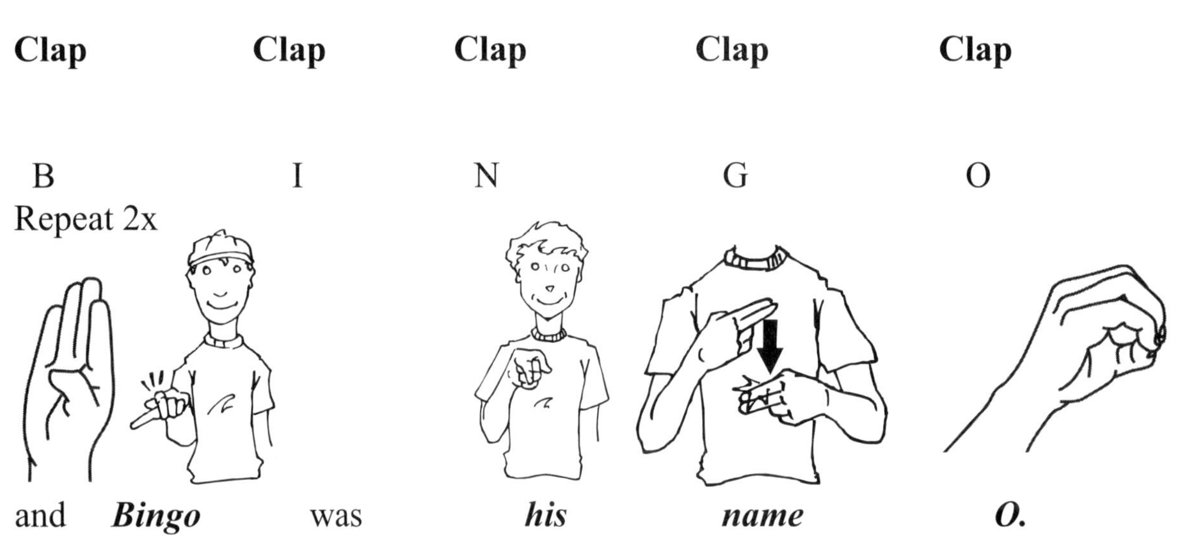

and ***Bingo*** was ***his*** ***name*** ***O.***

# "Buckle Bear Safety Song"

(Original Author Unknown, Illustrations Copyright©2003 Time to Sign, Inc.)

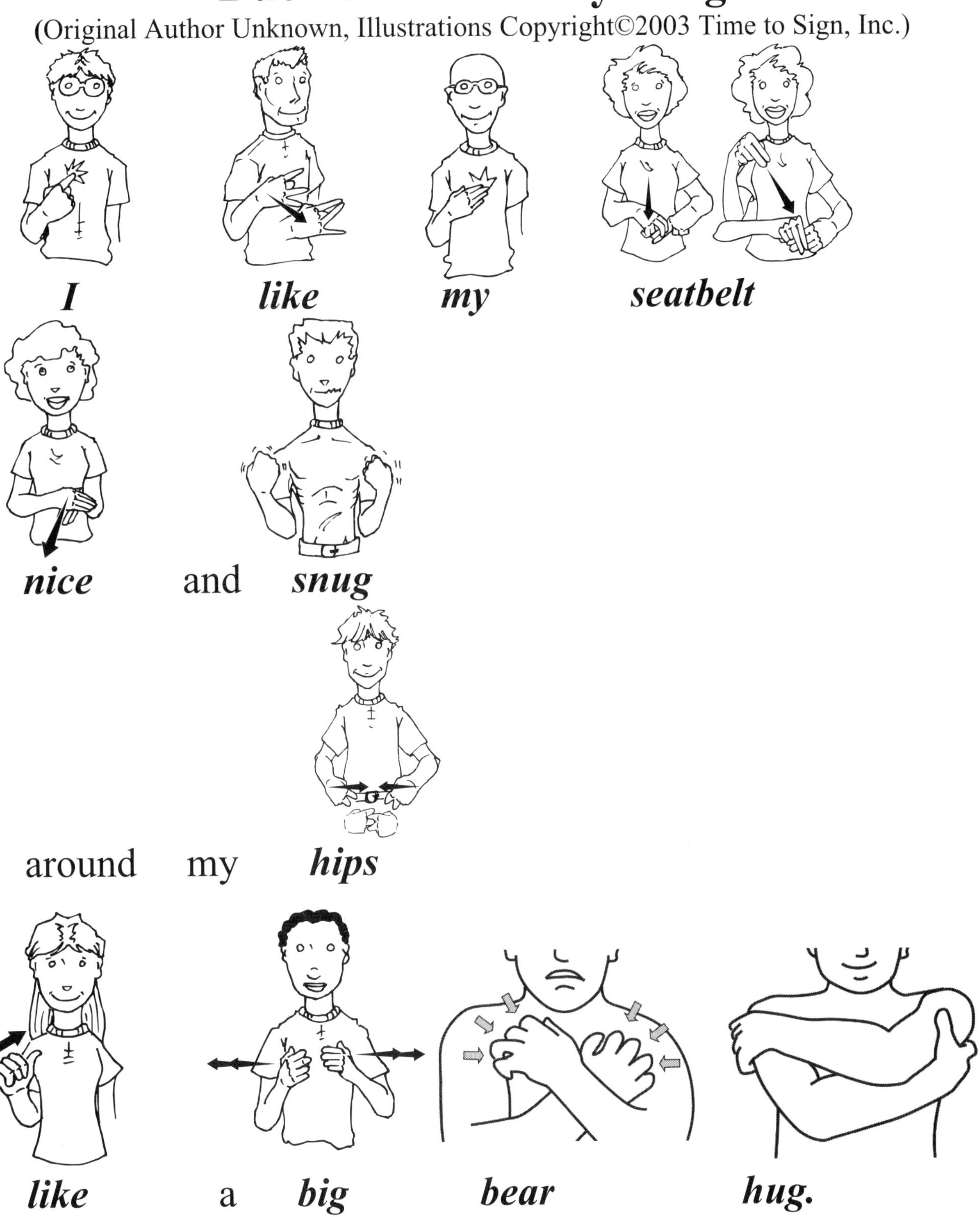

Time to Sign

I make it click
so the driver will know
I'm buckled up and ready to go.

# "Car Song"

(Original Author Unknown, Illustrations Copyright©2002 Time to Sign, Inc.)

***We*** ***like*** to ***travel*** ***in*** our ***car***
Hurrah, Hurrah.

A ***car*** ***can*** ***take*** ***us*** ***near*** or ***far***
Hurrah, Hurrah.

***We*** ***buckle*** up ***before*** ***we*** ***go,***

whether ***we're*** ***going*** ***fast*** or ***slow.***

So ***we'll*** ***all*** be ***safer*** while ***riding*** ***in*** ***our*** ***car***
Beep, beep, beep, beep
Beep, beep, beep, beep.

# “Down by the Station”

(Traditional, Illustrations Copyright©2002 Time to Sign, Inc.)

***Down*** by the ***station*** ***early*** in the ***morning***,

***see*** the ***little*** ***train*** ***cars*** all in a ***row.***

***Listen*** to the ***engineer*** pull the ***big*** ***whistle***

toot-toot, toot-toot! ***off*** ***we*** ***go***!

Choo-choo-choo-choo,

The ***train*** puffs ***down*** the ***track***.
(Bend arms at elbows and imitate chugging.)

***Now*** it's ***going*** ***forward***.
(Chug leaning forward.)

***Now*** it's ***chugging*** ***back***.
(Chug arms back to sitting position.)

***Now*** the ***bell*** is ringing.
(Imitate ringing clapper of bell.)

***Now*** the ***whistle*** blows.
(Imitate pulling chain of train whistle up and down.)
Chugging, chugging, chugging, chugging.
(Move bent arms back and forth.)

***Down*** the ***track*** it ***goes***!

# "Fruits Song"

(Copyright Time to Sign, Inc. 2002, Tune of Row, Row, Row Your Boat)

***Eat,*** ***eat,*** ***eat*** ***your*** ***fruits***

Everyday-
swipe hand along
cheek 3 times.

***every*** single ***day.***

Repeat 1x

***Eat,*** ***eat,*** ***eat*** ***your*** ***apples***

Everyday-
swipe hand along
cheek 3 times.

***every*** single ***day.***

Repeat 1x

***every*** single ***day.***

Repeat 1x

***Eat, eat, eat your grapes***

***every*** single ***day.***
Repeat 1x

***Eat, eat, eat your pears***

***every*** single ***day.***
Repeat 1x

***every*** single ***day.***
Repeat 1x

# *"I'm a Firefighter"*

(Original Author Unknown, Tune of "I'm a Little Teapot, Illustrations Copyright©2003 Time to Sign, Inc.)

***I*** can ***drive*** the ***fire truck***,

***fight*** ***fires***, ***too***,

and ***help*** to ***make*** things

***safe*** for ***you***.

# *"I'm a Police Officer"*

(Original Author Unknown, Tune of "I'm a Little Teapot, Illustrations Copyright©2003 Time to Sign, Inc.)

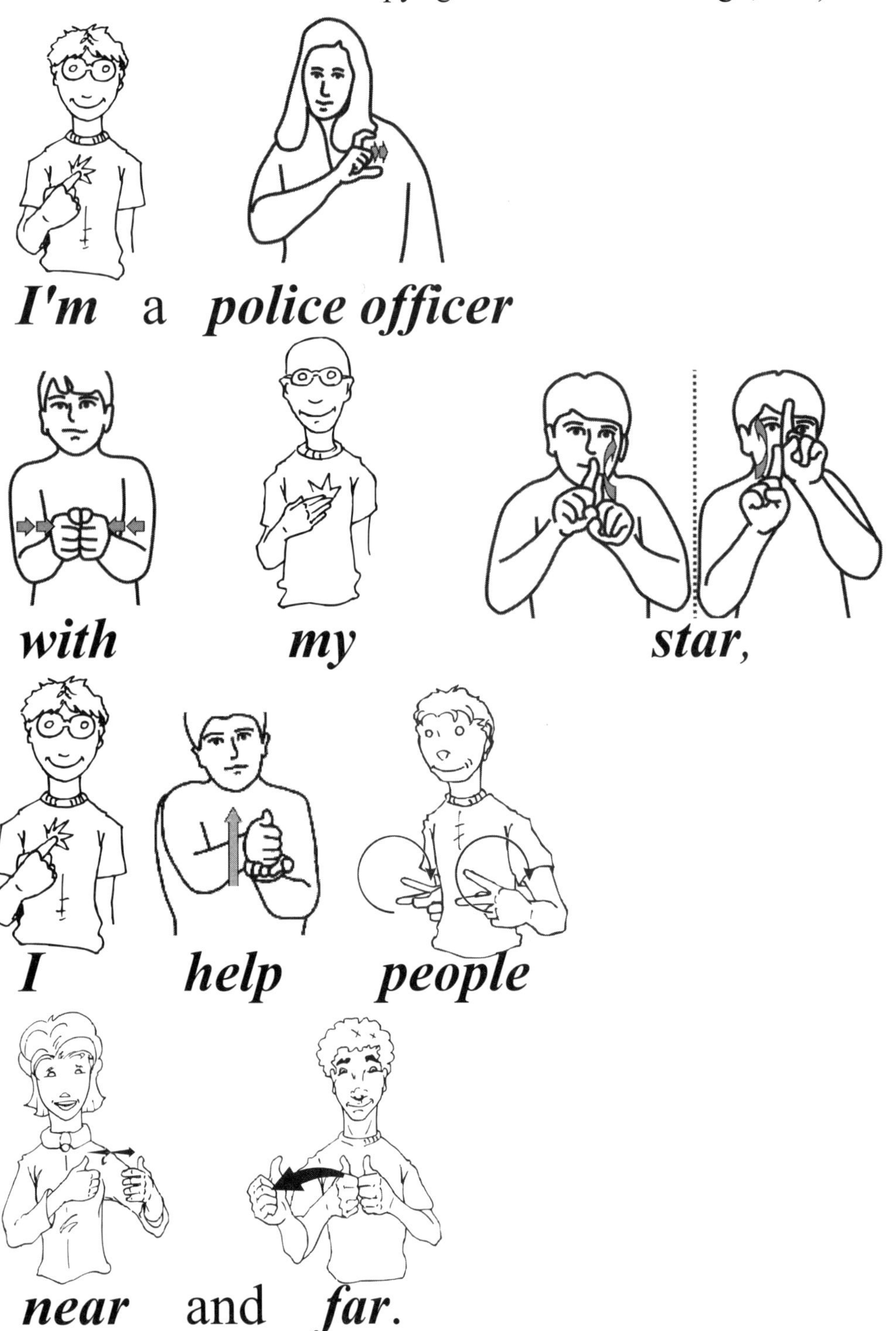

If ***you*** have a ***problem***,

***call*** on ***me***,

and ***I*** will be ***there***

 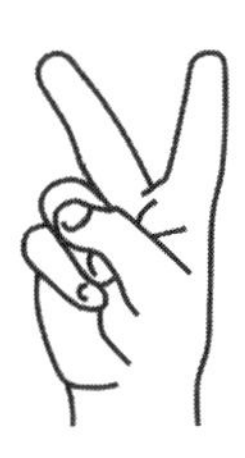 

***one***, ***two***, ***three***!

# "Make New Friends"

(Traditional, Illustrations Copyright©2002 Time to Sign, Inc.)

***Make*** ***new*** ***friends***, but ***keep*** the ***old***,

***one*** is ***silver*** and the ***other's*** ***gold***.

***Make*** ***new*** ***friends***, but ***keep*** the ***old***,

***one*** is ***silver*** and the ***other's*** ***gold***.

# “Mr. Sun”

(Traditional, Illustrations Copyright©2002 Time to Sign, Inc.)

Oh Mister ***Sun,*** ***sun,*** Mister ***Golden*** ***Sun***

***please*** ***shine*** ***down*** ***on*** ***me.***

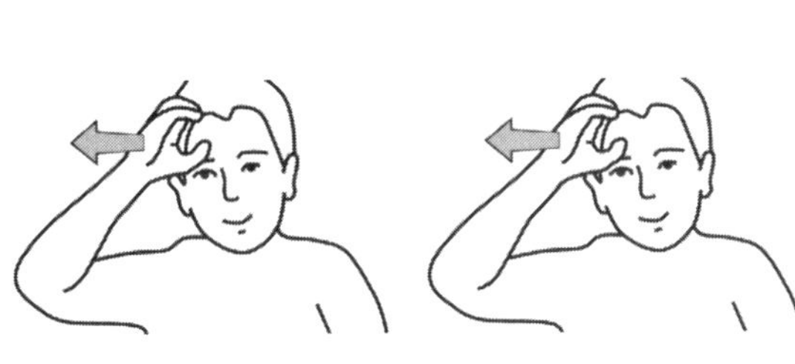

Oh Mister ***Sun,*** ***sun,*** Mister ***Golden*** ***Sun***

Time to Sign

*hiding behind* a *tree*.
These *little children* are *asking you*
to *please come out*
so *we can play with you.*

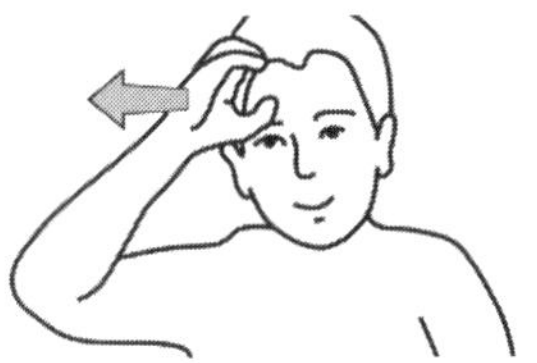

Oh Mister ***Sun,*** ***sun,*** Mister ***Golden*** ***Sun***

***please*** ***shine*** ***down,***

***please*** ***shine*** ***down,***

***please*** ***shine*** ***down*** ***on*** ***me.***

.

# *"Old MacDonald Had A Farm"*

(Traditional, Illustrations Copyright©2002 Time to Sign, Inc.)

***Old*** ***MacDonald*** had a ***farm,*** ee-eye, ee-eye oh.

And on his ***farm*** he had some ***chickens,*** ee-eye, ee-eye, oh.

With a ***cluck, cluck*** here and a ***cluck, cluck*** there,

here a ***cluck***, there a ***cluck,*** everywhere a ***cluck, cluck.***

***Old*** ***MacDonald*** had a ***farm,*** ee-eye, ee-eye oh.

***Old*** ***MacDonald*** had a ***farm,*** ee-eye, ee-eye oh.

And on his ***farm*** he had some ***ducks,*** ee-eye, ee-eye, oh

With a ***quack, quack*** here and a ***quack, quack*** there,

here a ***quack***, there a ***quack,*** everywhere a ***quack, quack.***

***Old*** ***MacDonald*** had a ***farm,*** ee-eye, ee-eye oh.

***Old*** ***MacDonald*** had a ***farm,*** ee-eye, ee-eye oh.

And on his ***farm*** he had some ***dogs***, ee-eye, ee-eye oh.

With a ***ruff, ruff*** here, and a ***ruff, ruff*** there,

here a ***ruff***, there a ***ruff***, everywhere a ***ruff, ruff.***

***Old*** ***MacDonald*** had a ***farm,*** ee-eye, ee-eye oh.

***Old*** ***MacDonald*** had a ***farm,*** ee-eye, ee-eye oh.

And on his ***farm*** he had some ***cats***, ee-eye, ee-eye oh.

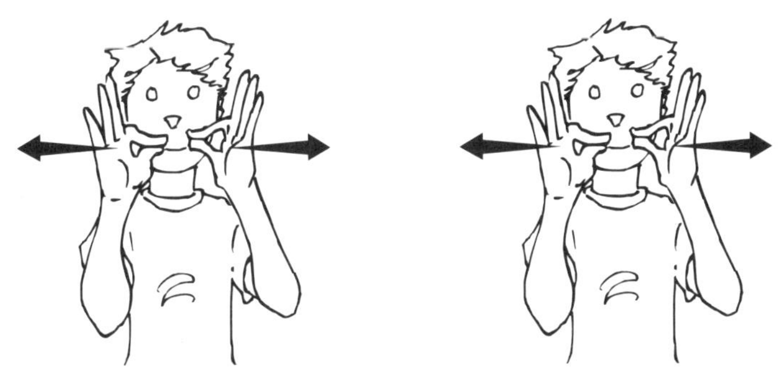

With a ***meow, meow*** here and a ***meow, meow*** there,

here ***meow***, there ***meow***, everywhere ***meow, meow*** .

***Old*** ***MacDonald*** had a ***farm,*** ee-eye, ee-eye oh.

***Old*** ***MacDonald*** had a ***farm,*** ee-eye, ee-eye oh.

And on his ***farm*** he had some ***pigs,*** ee-eye, ee-eye oh.

With an ***oink, oink*** here, and an ***oink, oink*** there,

here an ***oink***, there an ***oink***, everywhere an ***oink, oink.***

***Old*** ***MacDonald*** had a ***farm***, ee-eye, ee-eye oh.

***Old*** ***MacDonald*** had a ***farm***, ee-eye, ee-eye oh.

And on his ***farm*** he had some ***cows***, ee-eye, ee-eye oh.

With a ***moo, moo*** here, and a ***moo, moo*** there,

here a ***moo***, there a ***moo***, everywhere a ***moo, moo.***

***Old*** ***MacDonald*** had a ***farm***, ee-eye, ee-eye oh.

***Old*** ***MacDonald*** had a ***farm***, ee-eye, ee-eye oh.

And on his ***farm*** he had some ***horses***, ee-eye, ee-eye oh.

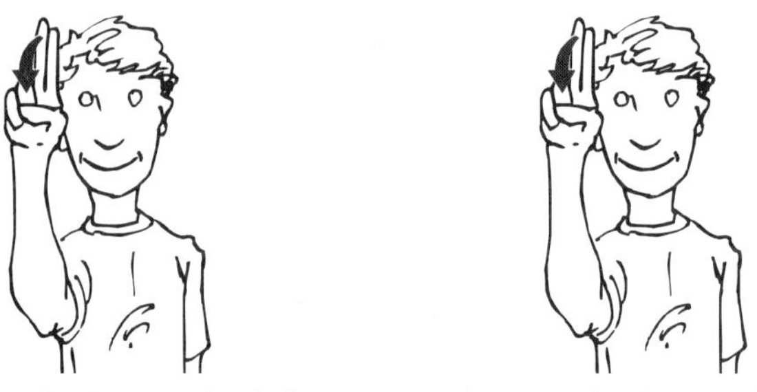

With a ***neigh, neigh*** here and a ***neigh, neigh*** there,

here ***neigh***, there ***neigh***, everywhere ***neigh, neigh***.

***Old*** ***MacDonald*** had a ***farm***, ee-eye, ee-eye oh.

***Old*** ***MacDonald*** had a ***farm***, ee-eye, ee-eye oh.

And on his ***farm*** he had some ***turkeys***, ee-eye, ee-eye oh.

With a ***gobble*** here and a ***gobble, gobble*** there,

here a ***gobble***, there a ***gobble***, everywhere a ***gobble, gobble.***

***Old*** ***MacDonald*** had a ***farm***, ee-eye, ee-eye oh.

# *"Seven Days"*

(Traditional, Illustrations Copyright©2002 Time to Sign, Inc.)

There are ***seven*** ***days***, there are ***seven*** ***days***,

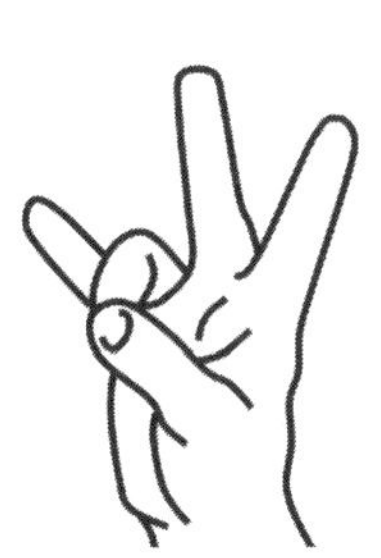

there are ***seven*** ***days*** in a ***week***.

***Sunday***, ***Monday***, ***Tuesday***, ***Wednesday***,

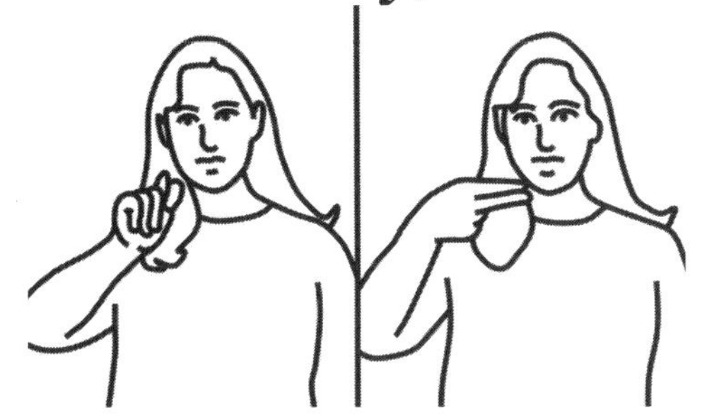
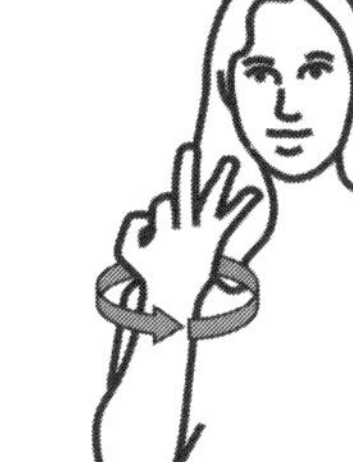

***Thursday***, ***Friday***, ***Saturday***.

# *"The Five Senses Song"*

(Original Author Unknown, Tune of "Old MacDonald Had a Farm", Illustrations Copyright©2002 Time to Sign, Inc.)

On my face I have two eyes; use them every day.
With a ***look***, ***look*** here, and a ***look***, ***look*** there,
Here a ***look***, there a ***look***, everywhere a ***look***, ***look***.
On my face I have two eyes; use them every day!

On my face I have a nose; use it all the time.
With a ***sniff***, ***sniff*** here, and a ***sniff***, ***sniff*** there,
Here a ***sniff***, there a ***sniff***, everywhere a ***sniff***, ***sniff***.
On my face I have a nose; use it all the time!

In my mouth I have a tongue; use it when I eat.
With a ***taste***, ***taste*** here, and a ***taste***, ***taste*** there,
Here a ***taste***, ***there*** a ***taste***, everywhere a ***taste***, ***taste***.
In my mouth I have a tongue; use it when I eat!

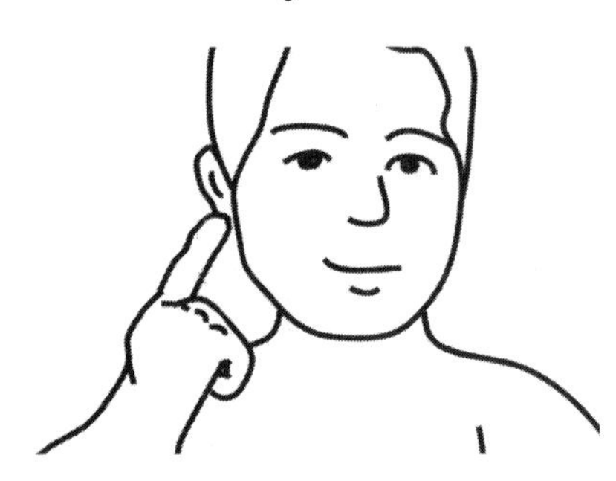

On my head I have two ears; listening all day long.
With a ***listen*** here, and a ***listen*** there,
Here a ***listen***, there a ***listen***, everywhere a ***listen***, ***listen***.
On my head I have two ears; listening all day long!

On my body I have skin; feeling cold and heat.
With a ***touch***, ***touch*** here, and a ***touch***, ***touch*** there,
Here a ***touch***, there a ***touch***, everywhere a ***touch***, ***touch***.
On my body I have skin; feeling cold and heat!

# *"Veggies Song"*

(Copyright©2002 Time to Sign, Inc., Tune of Row, Row, Row Your Boat)

***every*** single ***day.***

Repeat

***Eat, eat, eat your carrots***

***every*** single ***day.***
Repeat

***Eat, eat, eat your peas***

Everyday-
swipe hand along
cheek 3 times.

***every*** single ***day.***
Repeat

***Eat, eat, eat your vegetables***

Everyday-
swipe hand along
cheek 3 times.

***every*** single ***day.***
Repeat

# "We've Been Playing"

Original Author Unknown, illustrations Copyright©2002 Time to Sign, Inc.,Tune of "I've been working on the railroad")

***We've*** been ***playing*** on the ***playground***

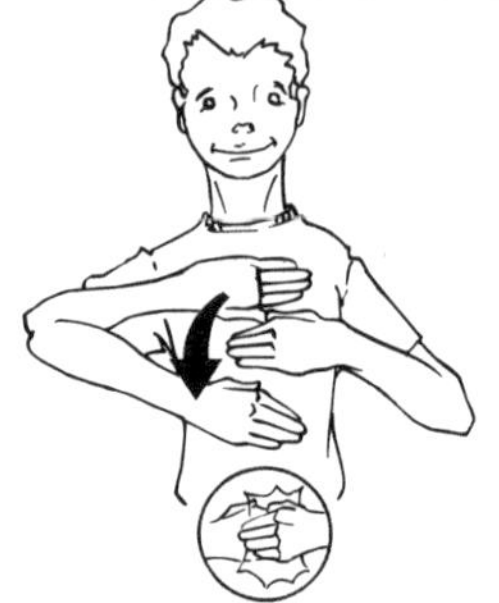

***all*** the ***morning*** long.

***We've*** been ***playing*** in the ***playground***

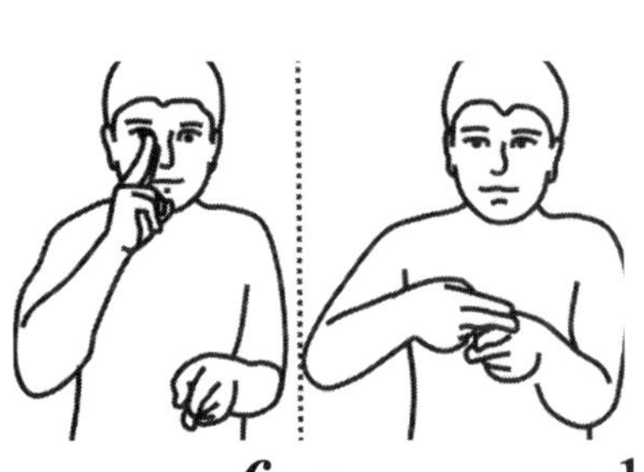
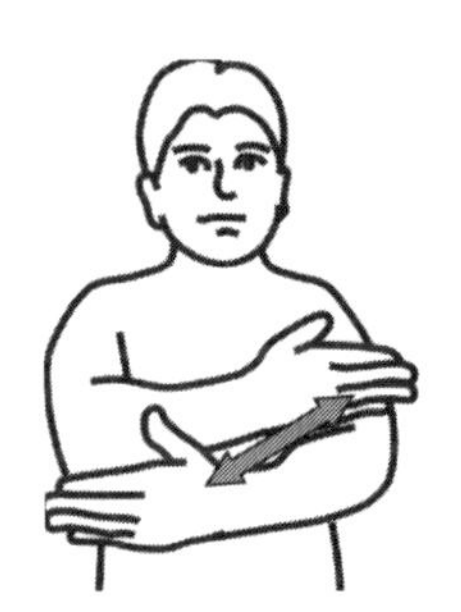

***having*** ***fun*** and ***singing*** songs.

***Now*** it's ***time*** to ***brush the dust off***,

***go*** in and ***eat*** our ***lunch***.

Then ***we'll*** ***brush our teeth*** and ***lay down,***

***look*** out ***here*** ***we*** ***come.***

# *"Wheels on the Bus"*

(Traditional, Illustrations Copyright©2002-2003 Time to Sign, Inc.)

The ***wheels on*** the ***bus*** ***go*** ***round*** and ***round,***

***round*** and ***round,*** ***round*** and ***round***

The wheels on the bus go round and round, (repeat)

***all*** ***through*** the ***town.***

The ***wipers*** ***on*** the ***bus*** ***go*** ***swish, swish, swish,***

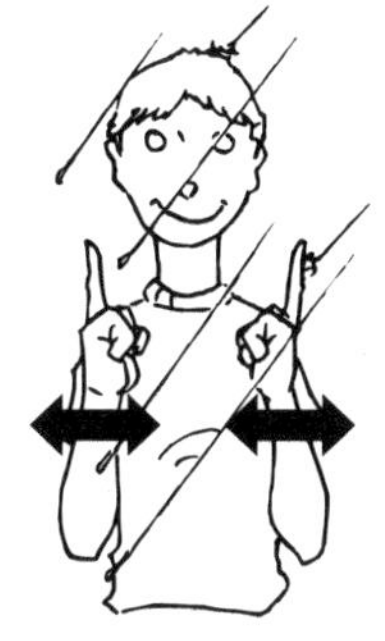

***swish, swish, swish,*** ***swish, swish, swish***

The wipers on the bus go swish, swish, swish, (repeat)

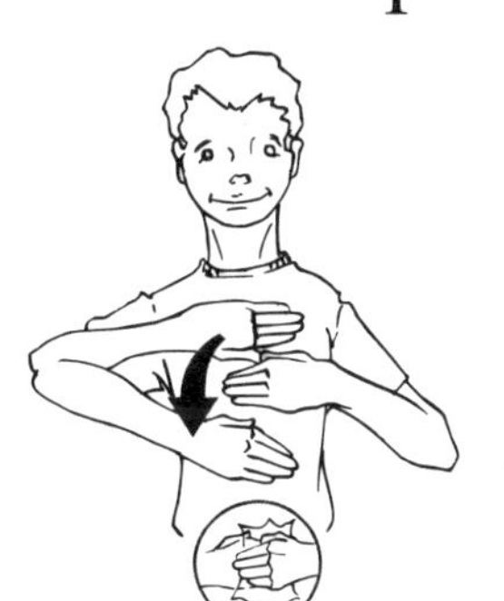

***all*** ***through*** the ***town.***

The ***horn*** ***on*** the ***bus*** ***goes*** ***beep, beep, beep,***

***beep, beep, beep,*** ***beep, beep, beep***

The horn on the bus goes beep, beep, beep, (repeat)

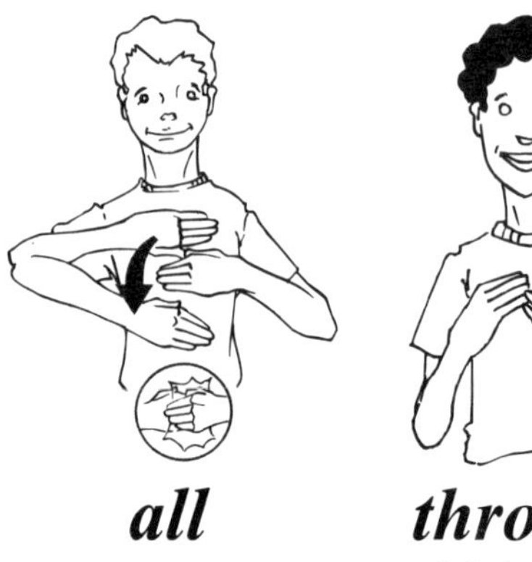

***all*** ***through*** the ***town.***

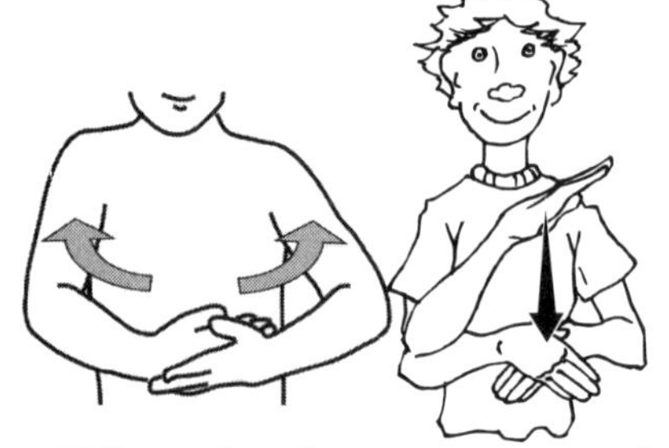

The ***baby*** ***on*** the ***bus*** ***goes*** ***waa, waa, waa,***

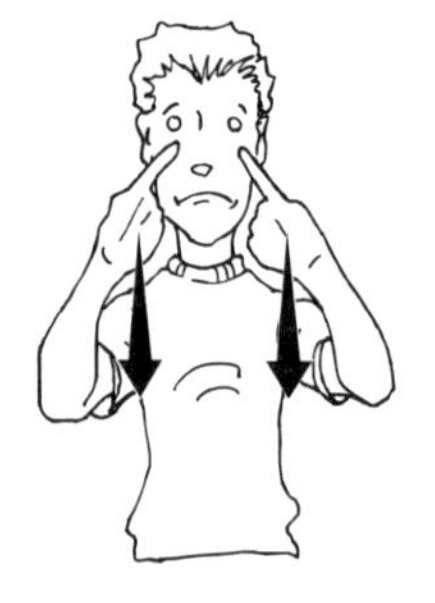
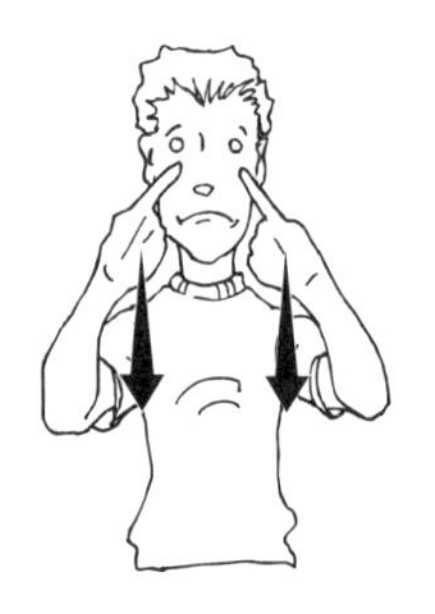

***waa, waa, waa,*** ***waa, waa, waa,***

The baby on the bus goes waa, waa, waa, (repeat)

***all*** ***through*** the ***town.***

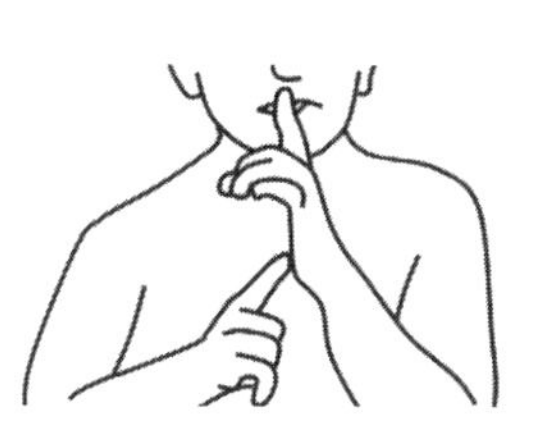

The ***mommy on*** the ***bus*** ***goes*** ***shh, shh, shh,***

***shh, shh, shh,*** ***shh, shh, shh***

The mommy on the bus goes shh, shh, shh, (repeat)

***all*** ***through*** the ***town.***

The ***driver*** ***on*** the ***bus*** ***goes*** ***move*** on ***back***,

***move*** on ***back***, ***move*** on ***back***

The driver on the bus goes move on back, (repeat)

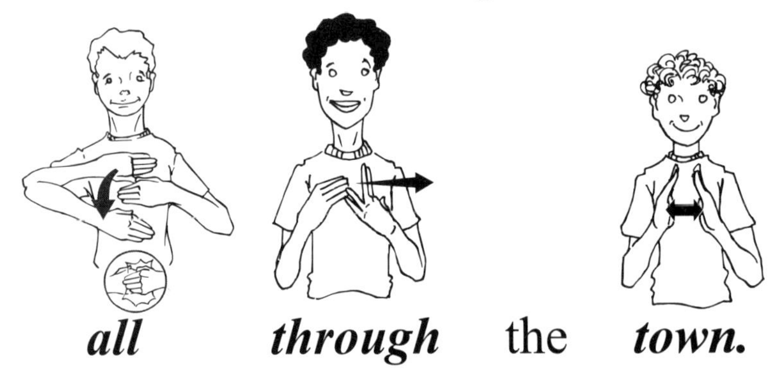

***all*** ***through*** the ***town.***

The ***wheels on*** the ***bus*** ***go*** ***round*** and ***round,***

***round*** and ***round,*** ***round*** and ***round***

The wheels on the bus go round and round, (repeat)

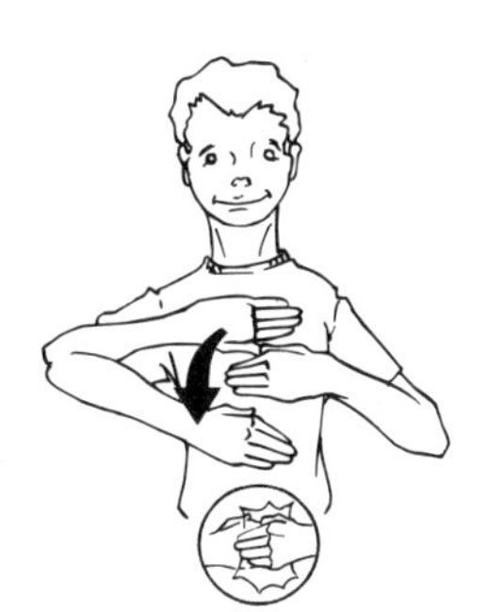

***all*** ***through*** the ***town.***

# *"You Are My Sunshine"*

(Traditional, Illustrations Copyright©2003 Time to Sign, Inc.)

***You*** are ***my*** ***sunshine***,

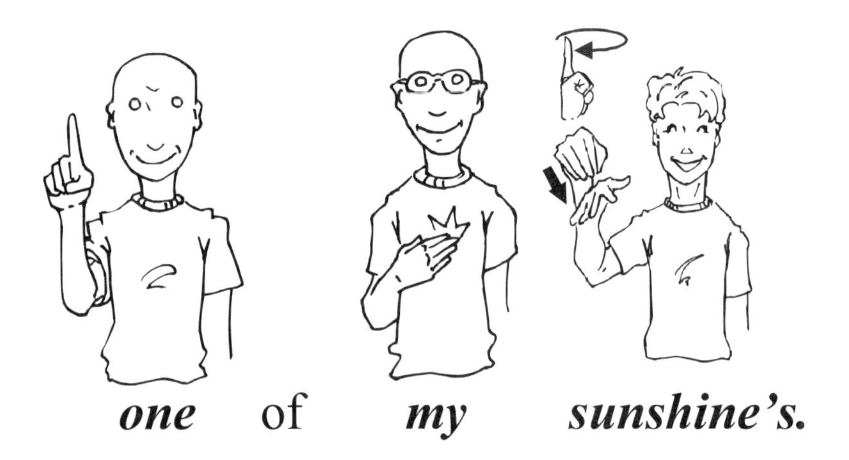

***You'll*** ***always*** ***know*** dear,

***how*** much ***I*** ***love*** ***you.***

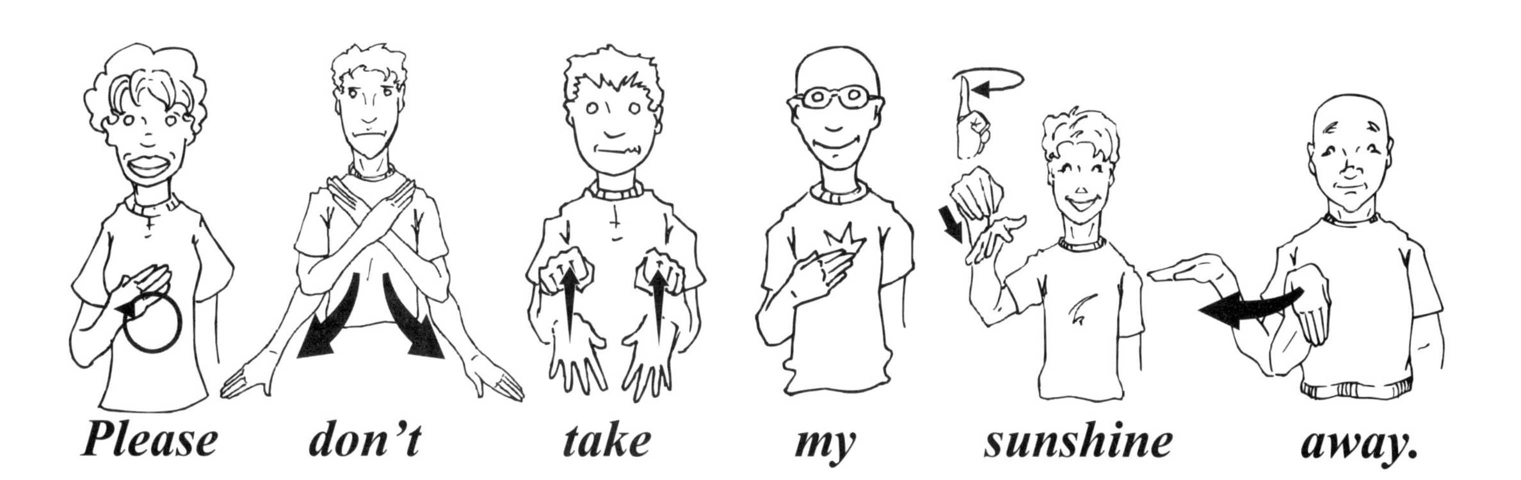

***Please*** ***don't*** ***take*** ***my*** ***sunshine*** ***away.***